BRAVO FOR LIFE'S
LITTLE IRONIES

Selected cartoons from

BUT THIS WAR HAD SUCH PROMISE

A *Doonesbury* Book

Bravo For Life's Little Ironies

by G. B. Trudeau

POPULAR LIBRARY • NEW YORK

WHAT'RE YOU GOING TO DO WITH THE MONEY YOU GOT FOR CHRISTMAS, BENJY?

SAVE IT. I WANT TO GO TO HARVARD MEDICAL SCHOOL ONE DAY.

ALL THE GUYS IN MY SCIENCE CLASS ARE GOING TO HARVARD MED. SCHOOL. WE'RE PLANNING TO OPEN A CLINIC IN SOUTHAMPTON AND MAKE FIVE OR SIX MILLION DOLLARS. THEN WE'RE GOING TO RETIRE AND START A COMMUNE IN THE BARBADOS.

BIG PLANS...
YOU BET. BUT WE'RE QUITE SERIOUS ABOUT IT.

WE TALK ABOUT IT OVER MILK AND COOKIES EVERY MORNING...
I SEE.

HEY, MARK, I'D LIKE YOU TO MEET SOMEONE... THIS IS THE GUY WHO'S STARTED THIS NEW COFFEEHOUSE

ER, HI.
REVEREND SCOT SLOAN'S THE NAME, SON! I'M THE FIGHTING YOUNG PRIEST WHO CAN TALK TO THE YOUNG.

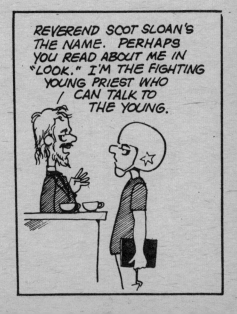

MY SPECIALTY, OF COURSE, IS SETTING UP DIALOGUES. OFTEN I AM SUCCESSFUL IN GETTING PEOPLE TO LOOK AT THEMSELVES HONESTLY AND MEANINGFULLY.

GOOD FOR YOU, SWEETHEART. ONE BLACK COFFEE TO GO.
©GB Trudeau

CHINESE!!
GBTrudeau

WOW!! SAY SOMETHING IN CHINESE!
WANNA PLAY PING PONG?
YEAH!
YOU'RE VERY IN THIS YEAR...

B.D., MIKE TELLS ME YOU SUPPORT THE CURRENT U.S. FOREIGN POLICY.
DARN RIGHT, I DO!

REALLY? WHAT BENEFITS DO YOU THINK U.S. INTRUSION HAS BROUGHT THE VIETNAMESE PEOPLE?
WHAT A DUMB QUESTION! WHY, WE'RE DOING GREAT THINGS FOR THOSE PEOPLE DEMOCRACYWISE. FOR EXAMPLE, THEY NOW HAVE FREE ELECTIONS!

HEE, HEE,
HEE!!

HA, HA!
HA, HA,
HA, HA,
HA!
O.K., LET ME
USE ANOTHER
EXAMPLE.
GBTrudeau

NEED ANY MORE HELP ON YOUR TERM PAPER?
NO, THANKS. I'M NOT GOING TO FINISH IT. I DECIDED LAST NIGHT TO DROP OUT OF SCHOOL AND GO TO VIETNAM.

WHAT?..
I'M TALKING TO MY R.O.T.C. OFFICER TODAY. IF I'M ACCEPTED, I WON'T HAVE TO FINISH MY TERM PAPER!

WELL, GOODBY OL' FRIEND! GOOD LUCK IN VIETNAM...
GOODBY, BERNIE. AND THANKS FOR YOUR ENCOURAGE-MENT. I'M GLAD AT LEAST SOME-BODY THINKS I'M DOING THE RIGHT THING...

LEAST I COULD DO. AFTER ALL, YOU ARE WHAT YOU ARE..
AND WHAT'S THAT?

WHY, A LUNATIC, OF COURSE..
OF COURSE.

FLY ME TO THE MOON...
TAKE CARE, BERNIE..
GBTrudeau

Dear Mom and Dad,
While I'm waiting for the next wave of Commies to attack, I thought I'd drop you a quick line.
U.S.

I arrived in Vietnam yesterday and I must say, I love it! I'm stationed at Firebase Bundy in the Delta and I've got my own bunker and machine gun!! Can you imagine?!
U.S.

'CAUSE... HEE, HEE... HE WANTED TO SEE TIME FLY! HAW! HA, HA, HA!

THAT'S ONE OF HER JOKES..
SHE'S A RIOT.
GBTrudeau

YOU KNOW WHAT BOTHERS ME, B.D.?– IT'S IMPOSSIBLE TO SEE THE ENEMY...
DON'T WORRY, GEORGE, HE'S OUT THERE..
GBTrudeau

AS A MATTER OF FACT, THERE'S CHARLIE NOW! BETTER GET DOWN, MAN...

ZING!
THAT'S ANOTHER THING! WHY DO WE ALWAYS CALL THE ENEMY "CHARLIE"? "CHARLIE" IS SUCH A BORING NAME!
ZING.
RAT TAT TAT

ZING!
WHY NOT "ARNOLD," OR "SEYMOUR," OR "PEABODY"?
YOU MEATHEAD.
RAT TAT TA
ZING!

GEORGE, WHAT'S GOING ON HERE? I'M TRYING TO GET SOME SLEEP...
BLAM!
ZING!
BLAM!
ZING!
BLAM!
V.C. GUNNER, B.D.!!

PESKY COMMIE!
BLAM!

AARRGGH! A TOUCH, I DO CONFESS IT! I FEAR I BREATHE MY LAST!

NOW WAIT A MINUTE...
HEE, HEE!
GBTrudeau

AH, FEBRUARY FIFTEENTH SIR...
GBTrudeau

FIFTEEN ENEMY DEAD, SIR.

HOWEVER!!.. EVEN IF I'M DESTINED TO DIE IN THIS CURSED JUNGLE, I STILL BELIEVE THIS WAR IS RIGHT, HONORABLE, AND A CREDIT TO AMERICA!

VELY NICE. HOW DO YOU FEEL ABOUT THE P.O.W. ISSUE?
©GBTrudeau

WHADDA YA LOWERING YOUR GUN FOR, CHARLIE? SCARED OF ME?
NO. WE'RE LOST..

LOST? YOU'RE JOKING..
NO, I'M NOT- WE'RE LOST. LEND ME YOUR JUNGLE MAP AND I'LL SEE IF I CAN FIGURE OUT WHERE WE ARE..

HEY, CHARLIE. HOW'D YOU COME TO LEARN ENGLISH?...
WHAT DO YOU MEAN? ENGLISH IS PRACTICALLY THE NATIONAL LANGUAGE IN VIETNAM.

IN CASE YOU DIDN'T KNOW, YOU RUNNING DOGS HAVE BEEN OCCUPYING OUR COUNTRY FOR FIFTEEN YEARS.. AND BY THE WAY, MY NAME'S PHRED, NOT CHARLIE...

I'M A V.C. TERRORIST. AND I'M A GOOD ONE, TOO! AIN'T NOBODY IN THESE PARTS WHO AIN'T HEARD OF "PHRED THE TERRORIST."

YESSIR, I CAN RAZE A HAMLET IN THIRTY SECONDS FLAT...
"PHRED THE TERRORIST."
GB Trudeau

PHRED, HOW COME YOU DECIDED TO BECOME A TERRORIST?..
HMM.. NOT SURE, REALLY, B.D...

PROBABLY BECAUSE MY FATHER WAS ONE. HE USED TO DO QUITE A JOB ON THE LOCAL FRENCH OUTPOSTS. DAD TAUGHT ME EVERYTHING I KNOW.

SIGH
Z-Z-Z

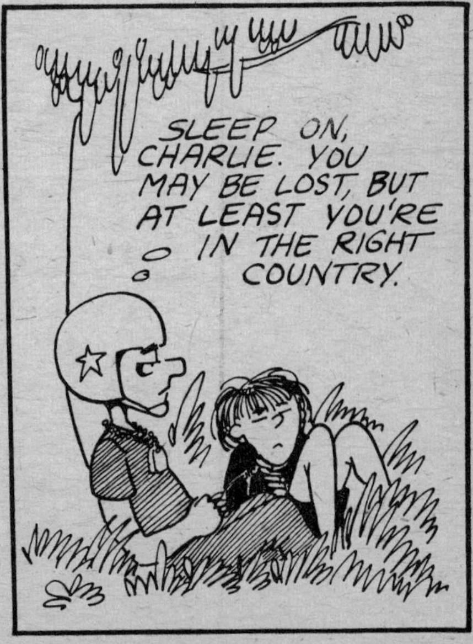
SLEEP ON, CHARLIE. YOU MAY BE LOST, BUT AT LEAST YOU'RE IN THE RIGHT COUNTRY.

ME, I'M THOUSANDS OF MILES FROM HOME, HUNGRY, TIRED, DISGRACED AND HUMILIATED. HOW COULD THINGS POSSIBLY GET ANY WORSE FOR ME?

Dear John...
GBTrudeau

WE ARE FORTUNATE TO HAVE MR. AGNEW HERE TONIGHT IN OUR STUDIO, AND HE'LL NOW SAY A FEW WORDS...

O.K., YOU SNOBS, THE PICNIC'S OVER...
GBTrudeau

YEAH, BUT IF HE'S SUCH A NICE GUY, WHY'D HE BECOME A TERRORIST?
WELL, IT WASN'T REALLY HIS FAULT...
HIS FAMILY PRESSURED HIM INTO IT...
GBTrudeau

DID I TELL YOU I'M THINKING OF CHANGING MY NAME?
WHATEVER FOR? WHAT'S WRONG WITH "RUFUS"?

WELL.. IT'S A LITTLE TRITE. EVERY OTHER KID ON MY BLOCK IS CALLED "RUFUS." I GUESS IT'S A CULTURAL THING...

ANYWAY, I'VE DECIDED TO GET ANOTHER NAME.. I THINK I WANT A NAME THAT REFLECTS MY ENORMOUS STRENGTH OF CHARACTER...

GOT ONE YET?

HOW DOES "THOR" GRAB YOU?

G.B.Trudeau

O.K., THOR, I'VE GOT A TOUGH ONE FOR YOU... WHAT'S THE SQUARE ROOT OF 144?

ELEVEN.
UH... NO, NOT QUITE. ELEVEN IS THE SQUARE ROOT OF 121. TRY AGAIN.

WHAT CAN I DO FOR YOU, ZONKER?
WELL, MIKE, I'M THINKING I'D LIKE TO WORK FOR THE PAPER.
TAP TAP

WORK FOR THE PAPER? ZONKER, WHAT DO YOU KNOW ABOUT REPORTING?
LOTS! LISTEN TO THIS!

PATRONAGE JOBS?.. THAT'S A PRETTY SERIOUS THING TO ACCUSE PRESIDENT KING OF..

WELL, THAT'S WHAT I HEARD. AS INVESTIGATIVE REPORTERS, I THINK WE OUGHT TO LOOK INTO IT.

AFTERNOON. WE'RE FROM THE CAMPUS NEWS. IS THE PRESIDENT IN?

UH-HUH, YOU'RE EXPECTED.

AHA!
A CALL
TO ARMS!
©GBTrudeau

TAT-TAT
RAT-TAT
TAT
TAT
TAT
Nonetheless,
he does
seem to
enjoy his
work.

SAY, DID YOU GUYS HEAR THAT THE PRESIDENT SAID THAT THE BOYS IN THE 'NAM ARE IN DEFENSIVE POSTURES?
RIGHT!
PRESS

PRETTY FAR OUT DEFENSIVE POSTURES!
BOY, DOES THAT MAN JIVE! HE SURE DOESN'T KNOW MUCH ABOUT WHAT'S GOING ON OVER HERE.
PRESS

WHAT A FOOLISH HOMBRE!
I'LL SAY! WHY'D YA SUPPOSE PEOPLE VOTE FOR HIM?
PRESS

HE KNOWS HOW TO HANDLE PUNKS LIKE YOU.
PRESS
©BTrudeau

IT'S ANOTHER HOT DAY HERE AT FIREBASE BUNDY AS B.D. MANS HIS POST WITH FORTITUDE AND BRAVADO.
BLAM! BLAM!
RAT-A-TAT-TAT. TAT!

BUT THE HOURS OF VIOLENCE AND STRESS ARE BEGINNING TO TAKE THEIR TOLL AS B.D.'S NERVES ARE STRETCHED TO THE BREAKING POINT... TENSE... NERVOUS..
BLAM! BLAM!
RAT-A-TAT TAT TAT

HEY, CAP'N! WE IN SAIGON YET?
NO, DUMMY, OF COURSE NOT! THESE'RE THE OUTSKIRTS!
PRESS

WELL, LOOK, MAN, I'VE GOTTA GET PIX OF THE CITY. SO TELL ME WHEN WE'RE IN SAIGON PROPER.
PRESS

BUT THINGS ARE GOING TO CHANGE, MIKE! YOU'LL SEE! MY FORMULA IS JUST THE BEGINNING! I SEE A DAY WHEN WEREWOLVES WILL BE ACCEPTED! YES, I SEE A DAY WHEN THEY WILL BE ADMIRED AND RESPECTED!

I SEE A DAY WHEN YOU'RE PUT AWAY.
©BTrudeau